# Zig and Zag

by Liza Charlesworth

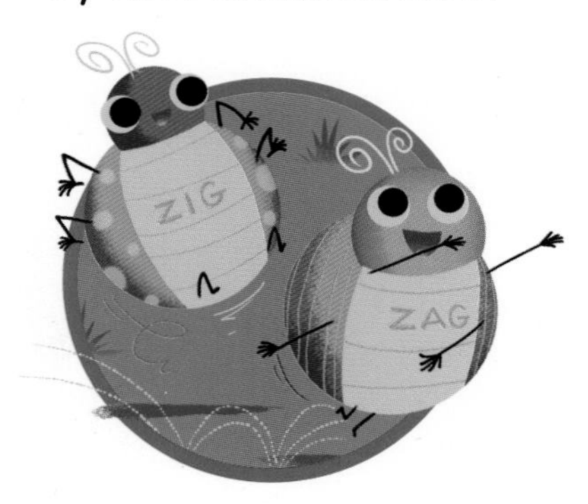




ISBN: 978-1-338-84426-9

Art Director: Tannaz Fassihi; Designer: Cynthia Ng; Illustrated by Kevin Zimmer


3 4 5 6 7 68 26 25 24

Printed in Jiaxing, China. First printing, June 2022.

SCHOLASTIC

It is Zig.
Zig is a fun bug!

It is Zag.
Zag is a fun bug!

Zig and Zag hop
with a hen.
Hop, hop!

Zig and Zag run
with a ram.
Run, run!

Zig and Zag dig
with a dog.
Dig, dig!

Zig and Zag mop
with a man.
Mop, mop!

Zig and Zag sit on top of a big, red bus.
Sit, sit!

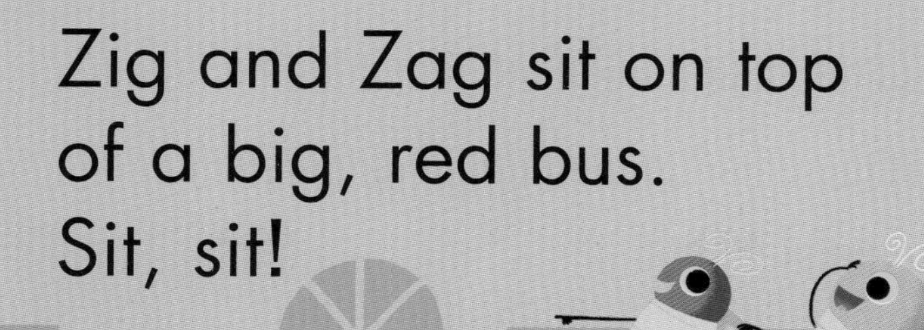

Zig and Zag
get gum.
Yum, yum!

Zig and Zag go up.
Up, up!

POP, POP!

Zig and Zag go down.
Down, down!

Zig and Zag hit a tin pot!
But it is not sad.

The tin pot is wet.
The tin pot is fab.
Wet, wet! Fab, fab!

# Read & Review

Invite your learner to point to each short-vowel word and read it aloud.

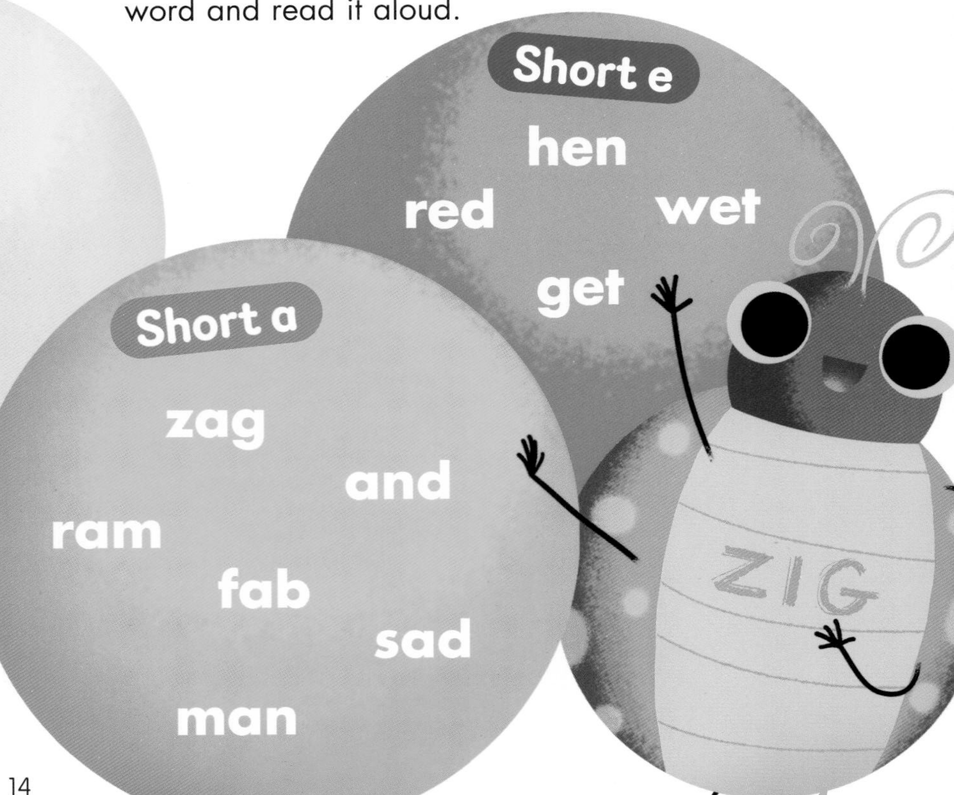

Short i
dig
in
zig
is
it
hit
big
tin
sit
Short o
on
hop
dog
not
pot
top
lot
mop
pop
Short u
bus
run
yum
gum
up
but
fun
bug

# Fun Fill-Ins

Read the sentences aloud, inviting your learner to complete them using the short-vowel words in the box.

hen   Zag   tin   up   dog

1. Zig's pal is ________.
2. Zig and Zag hop with a ________.
3. Zig and Zap dig with a ________.
4. Zig and Zag got gum and went ________!
5. Zig and Zag fell in a pot made of ________.